High-Frequenc
READERS™
W9-BSB-196

We Are Painting

Written by Francie Alexander
Illustrated by Michael Grejniec

Scholastic Inc.
New York Toronto London Auckland Sydney
Mexico City New Delhi Hong Kong

No part of this publication may be reproduced in whole or in part, or stored in a retrieval system, or transmitted in any form or by any means, electronic, mechanical, photocopying, recording, or otherwise, without written permission of the publisher. For information regarding permission, write to Scholastic Inc., Education Group, 555 Broadway, New York, NY 10012.

ISBN 0-439-13987-2

Copyright © 1999 by Scholastic Inc. All rights reserved. Published by Scholastic Inc. SCHOLASTIC and associated logos are trademarks and/or registered trademarks of Scholastic Inc.

17 16

Printed in the U.S.A.

10/0
23

First Scholastic clubs printing, November 1999

We are painting **green** grass.

We are painting 5 **red** flowers.

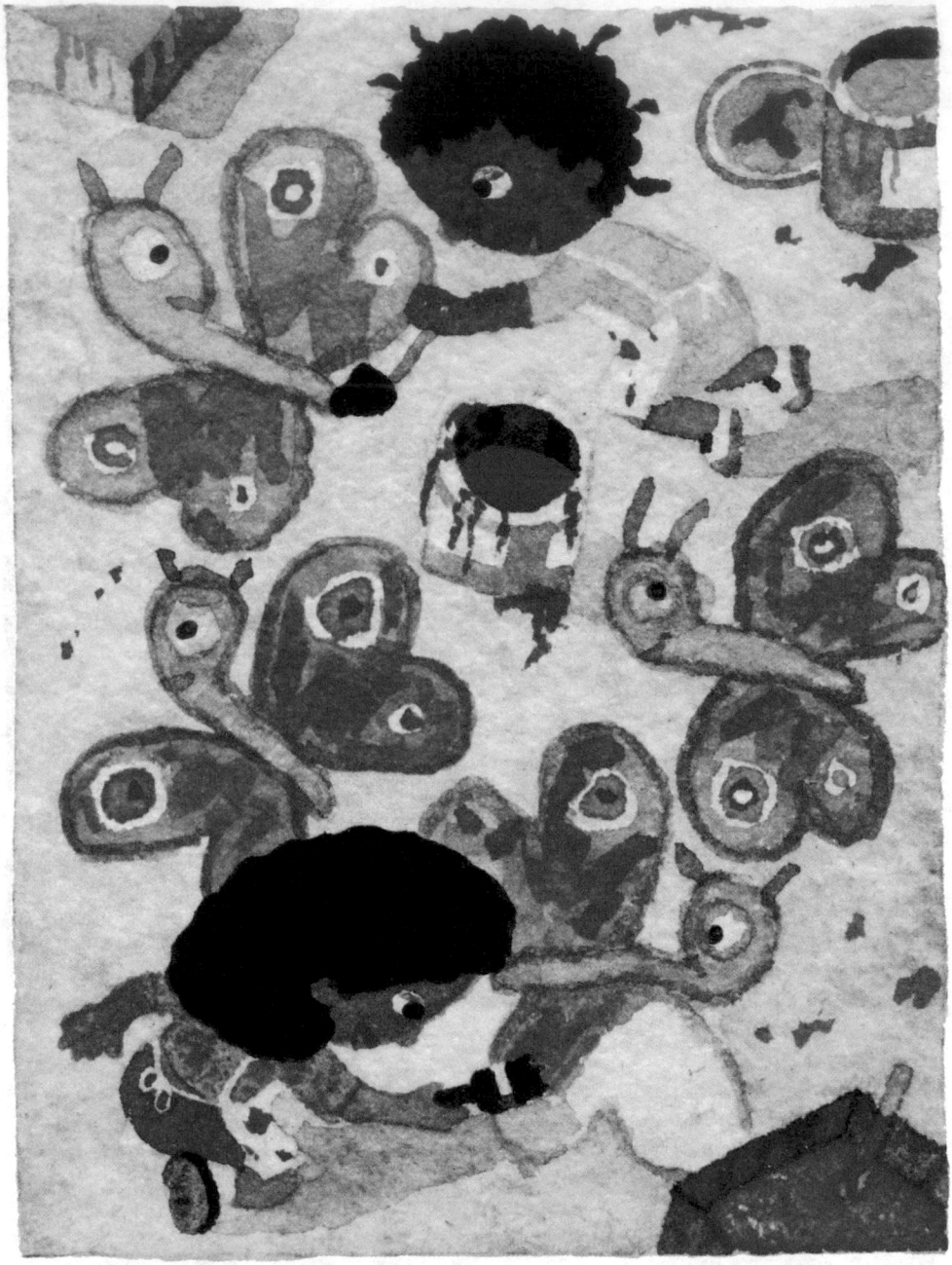

We are painting 4 **orange** butterflies.

We are painting 3 **blue** birds.

We are painting 2 **black** horses.

We are painting 1 yellow sun.

We are painting!